RUM AND THE SMALL ISLES

A LANDSCAPE FASHIONED BY GEOLOGY

©Scottish Natural Heritage 2004

ISBN 1 85397 370

A CIP record is held at the British Library

NP3K0304

Acknowledgements

Authors: Kathryn Goodenough (BGS) and Tom Bradwell (BGS)

Text on pages 20, 21 & 22: Alan McKirdy (SNH)

Text on page 35: Alison Grant

Series editor: Alan McKirdy (SNH)

Photography:

BGS 5 bottom, 9, 23, 34; **Martin Colbeck/Oxford Scientific** 5 top; **C.H. Emeleus** 4;

Lorne Gill/SNH 8, 10, 12, 15, 16, 17, 19, 21, 26, 28, 29, 32, 33; **A. Graham Leslie** 24;

Susan Loughlin 13; **Patricia & Angus Macdonald/SNH** 7, 11, 14, 18, 27, 35 bottom, back cover;

John MacPherson front cover, frontispiece; **Alan McKirdy** 20;

National Trust for Scotland 22 top, 22 bottom, 35 top; **Rum Excavation Project** 30.

Illustrations:

Elizabeth Pickett/BGS © NERC except for **BGS Drawing Office** © NERC 3; **Craig Ellery** page 2.

Further copies of this book and other publications can be obtained from:

The Publications Section,

Scottish Natural Heritage,

Battleby, Redgorton, Perth PH1 3EW

Tel: 01738 444177 Fax: 01738 827411

E-mail: pubs@snh.gov.uk

Web site: www.snh.org.uk

Front cover image:

View of Rum from the mainland

Back cover image:

Bloodstone Hill, Orval and the Rum Cuillin, Isle of Rum

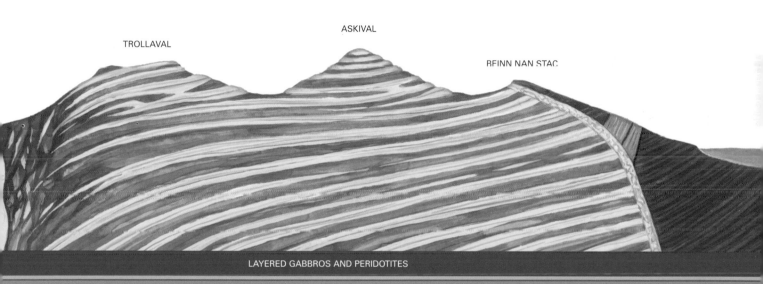

TROLLAVAL ASKIVAL BEINN NAN STAC

LAYERED GABBROS AND PERIDOTITES

The mountainous, wild landscape of the Isle of Rum has long been a mecca for geologists. For such a small island, the range of scenery is truly remarkable - from the jagged peaks of Askival and Hallival in the east, to the rounded hills of Orval and Ard Nev in the west, and the low "stepped" topography north of Kinloch Glen. As we will see, these features can be attributed to a geological history that stretches back nearly 3000 million years and includes deserts and ocean floors, volcanoes and glaciers.

Rum Through Time

RECENT TIMES		People arrived on Rum nearly 9,000 years ago and have lived on the islands ever since.
QUATERNARY 2.4 million years up to and including recent times		After 2.4 million years, the climate cooled dramatically, plunging Scotland into an 'Ice Age'. Very cold glacial episodes were interspersed with warmer periods. During the last main glacial period, from 30,000 to 15,000 years ago, ice moving westwards from the mainland covered Rum and the Small Isles. From 13,000 to 11,000 years ago small corrie glaciers existed on the peaks of Rum, but after 11,000 years ago the ice melted and vegetation began to recolonise the islands.
NEOGENE 2.4 to 24 million years ago		Tropical conditions were widespread, although the climate cooled as the Ice Age approaches.
PALAEOGENE 24 to 65 million years ago		Volcanoes developed on Rum and Skye, pouring lava onto the Earth's surface. Some magma cooled below the surface to form granites and gabbros.
CRETACEOUS 142 to 65 million years ago		A shallow sea known as the Sea of the Hebrides covered the area of modern-day Rum. The sediments that were deposited in this sea have largely been eroded away, and are not preserved on Rum.
JURASSIC PERIOD 206 to 142 million years ago		Rapid sea level change marked the beginning of this period, flooding much of Scotland. Dinosaurs roamed the coastal fringes and marine turtles, crocodiles and plesiosaurs swarm in the sea.
TRIASSIC 206 to 248 million years ago		Western Scotland was a low-lying area, with a warm, tropical climate. Sandstones containing plant fossils were laid down in rivers that flowed across the land. These sandstones can still be seen in northern Rum.
PERMIAN 248 to 290 million years		Deserts formed around the margins of present-day Scotland, but rocks from this time are not preserved on Rum.
CARBONIFEROUS 290 to 354 million years		Scotland sat astride of the equator. Tropical forests covered parts of Scotland. Decaying organic matter from these forests accumulated to form coals in central Scotland, but on Rum no new rocks were formed.
DEVONIAN 354 to 433 million years		Rum lay within an area of high ground where no new rocks were formed, whilst sandstones and limestones were deposited in the surrounding rivers and shallow seas.
SILURIAN 443 to 417 million years		Continental collision led to the formation of a great mountain chain in Scotland, but this part of the geological history is not preserved on Rum.
ORDOVICIAN 495 to 443 million years		Continental collision led to the formation of a great mountain chain in Scotland, but this part of the geological history is not preserved on Rum.
CAMBRIAN 495 to 545 million years		Quartz-rich sandstones and limestones formed in shallow seas. These rocks are seen on Skye and along the north-west coast, but not on Rum.
PRECAMBRIAN Before 545 million years		The basement of Rum, the Lewisian gneisses, formed nearly 3000 million years ago and were then deformed and metamorphosed during huge mountain-building events. Following these events, the Torridonian sandstones were laid down about 1000 million years ago on the beds of rivers flowing over a rocky landscape.

Geological Map of Rum and the Small Isles

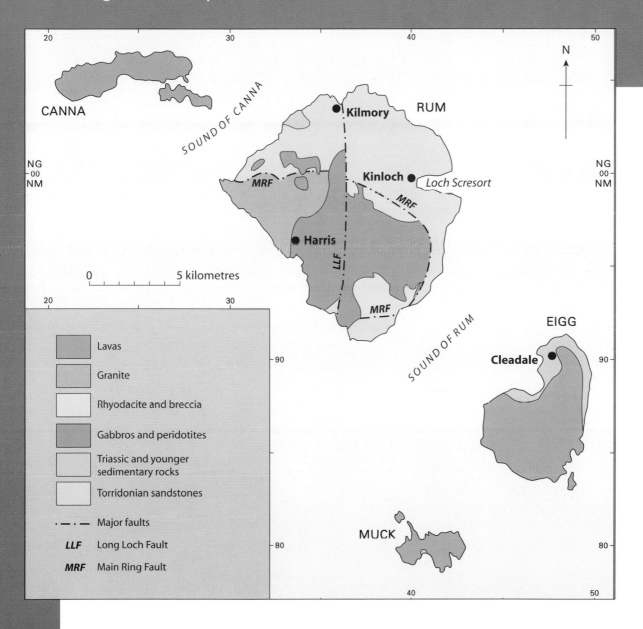

Legend:

- Lavas
- Granite
- Rhyodacite and breccia
- Gabbros and peridotites
- Triassic and younger sedimentary rocks
- Torridonian sandstones
- –·–· Major faults
- *LLF* Long Loch Fault
- *MRF* Main Ring Fault

0 ___ 5 kilometres

CANNA

SOUND OF CANNA

Kilmory

RUM

MRF

Kinloch

Loch Scresort

MRF

Harris

LLF

MRF

SOUND OF RUM

EIGG

Cleadale

MUCK

N

NG 00 NM

Setting the Scene

The history of Rum began nearly 3000 million years ago, when some of the oldest rocks in the world were formed - the Lewisian gneisses. These are metamorphic rocks, which were formed when even older granitic rocks were buried and heated deep beneath the Earth's surface. They can be seen in a few scattered outcrops on Rum.

By about 1100 million years ago, the Lewisian gneisses had been uplifted by immense movements within the Earth. Erosion on the surface had worn away these rocks to a bare, hummocky land surface looking rather like that of much of the Outer Hebrides today. The area which today makes up Scotland then lay much closer to the equator and had a warm, arid climate. Torrential rivers flowing across this landscape deposited sand and pebbles that accumulated into a pile of sediment many kilometres in thickness. As the sand and pebbles were compressed under the weight of the overlying sediment they formed a sequence of rocks, known as the Torridonian.

At that time, the land that now makes up the Isle of Rum was part of a huge supercontinent. After deposition of the Torridonian sandstones, this area remained fairly stable for many millions of years, during which time the rocks that make up much of the Highlands today were laid down near the margin of the supercontinent. Scotland was separated from the rest of modern Europe by an ocean that gradually narrowed, through the process of continental drift - until England and Scandinavia collided with Scotland around 430 million years ago.

The collision of two continents created a mountain range similar in scale to the Himalayas

This continental collision led to the formation of a mountain range that may have been as high as the modern-day Alps. The eroded remnants of this mountain chain form much of the Highlands today.

The next chapter in Rum's story began some 250 million years ago, in the Triassic Period, the mountains had been largely eroded away, and the western side of Scotland was a low-lying, arid area with a tropical climate. Sand and pebbles were eroded from higher land to the east and carried westwards by rivers, to be deposited on lower ground where they eventually formed sedimentary rocks. These rocks look similar to the Torridonian sandstones, but the presence of plant fossils indicates that they are much younger.

Triassic sedimentary rocks on top of Torridonian sandstones, Glen Shellesder

AS THE CONTINENT IS STRETCHED, CRACKS KNOWN
AS FAULTS DEVELOP IN THE EARTH'S CRUST

LAVA FLOWS OUT
OVER A WIDE AREA

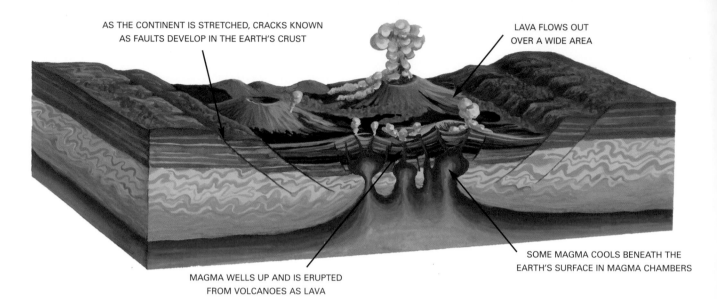

MAGMA WELLS UP AND IS ERUPTED
FROM VOLCANOES AS LAVA

SOME MAGMA COOLS BENEATH THE
EARTH'S SURFACE IN MAGMA CHAMBERS

For over 100 million years, during the Jurassic and Cretaceous periods, the Hebridean area remained close to sea level, with periodic incursions of the sea. During this time sediments, which later formed rocks such as limestones, sandstones and mudstones, were deposited. These rocks can be seen on the neighbouring island of Eigg, but on Rum they were removed by erosion that occurred when the area was raised up above sea level at the beginning of the Palaeogene Period some 65 million years ago.

The beginning of the Palaeogene Period was a key time in the geological history of Rum. Forces operating deep within the Earth began to pull apart the huge continent that included Scotland. As the continental mass was stretched, the Earth's crust began to crack. Magma, formed by the melting of rock many kilometres below the Earth's surface, welled up through these cracks in the crust and erupted from volcanoes. This magma spread out over much of the area in lava flows similar to those seen on Iceland today. Meanwhile, beneath the volcanoes, huge bodies of magma accumulated

in magma chambers deep within the Earth's crust. This magma slowly cooled and crystallised to form igneous rocks such as granite and gabbro. Much of the Isle of Rum represents the eroded remains of one of these volcanoes that formed 60 million years ago. Modern techniques used to date rocks accurately have showed us that the active lifetime of the Rum volcano was very short in geological terms - probably only a few hundred thousand years. The volcanic rocks of Rum have been intensely studied by geologists over the last 100 years, allowing us to understand in detail how the Rum volcano evolved. The volcanic features are described in more detail in the following pages.

By 55 million years ago, the volcanoes of northwest Scotland had ceased to erupt, and volcanic activity had shifted farther to the west as the North Atlantic began to open. The youngest volcanic rock still preserved in Scotland is the lava flow that now forms the distinctive Sgùrr of Eigg.

The gabbro peak of Hallival has been shaped by the action of glaciers over the last 2 million years

During the next 50 million years, the area around Rum underwent periodic erosion in a mostly warm, sub-tropical climate. This continued until about 2.4 million years ago, when the climate cooled dramatically and glaciers formed in Scotland. The landscape of Rum owes its appearance largely to the action of these glaciers; the corries, sharp peaks and deep U-shaped valleys on the island are all products of glacial erosion. During the last 2 million years glaciers have repeatedly scoured away soils and younger sediments, leaving the underlying rocks spectacularly exposed. Since about 750,000 years ago, intensely cold glacial episodes have been interspersed with brief warm interglacial periods. At the peak of one of these glacial episodes the whole island would have been almost completely covered by an ice sheet flowing from the mainland westwards. The most recent of these major glaciations was at its peak only 20,000 years ago. Around 11,500 years ago the climate warmed rapidly to give the temperate, maritime, conditions experienced today. Following the melting of the ice, much of the west of Scotland rose up as it adjusted to the removal of the weight of the glaciers, and hence the relative sea level fell rapidly. The sea level around Rum has continued to fall gradually over the last 6000 years or so as the island steadily rises.

Ancient Rivers on Rum

The 'stepped' landscape formed by the Torridonian sandstones of northern Rum

The reddish-brown Torridonian sandstones are best seen in the part of Rum north of Kinloch, although they also occur along the coast in the southeast of the island. They are sedimentary rocks – rocks that formed by the accumulation of large amounts of sediments such as sand. Northern Rum has a gently 'stepped' landscape, with obvious layers in the rock that are gently inclined down towards the northwest. When the sediments were originally laid down, nearly 1000 million years ago, they would have formed flat layers of sand and pebbles. Each layer represented an episode where a river flooded and deposited sediment across a floodplain. Later earth movements have led to these layers becoming tilted.

Because the sandstones were originally deposited in seasonal rivers, rather than deep in lakes or oceans, they were exposed to the air. This meant that iron particles in the sandstones became oxidised, in a process similar to rusting, producing a characteristic red-brown colour. In the south and southeast of Rum, the sandstones are interlayered with mudstones that were deposited in lakes and these rocks are typically grey rather than red-brown in colour.

The sedimentary rocks are softer than the rocks that make up the rest of Rum, and so they have been easily eroded, forming less mountainous areas. Most of the younger sedimentary rocks that once lay on top of the Torridonian have now been eroded away completely, but a small area of sandstones of Triassic age can still be found on Monadh Dubh in northwestern Rum, to the north of Glen Shellesder. These sandstones contain the poorly preserved remains of 250 million year-old plants.

The Rum Volcano

The jagged peak of Askival in the foreground, with Trollaval on the right and Ainshval beyond

An aerial view of Rum, showing the rounded western hills of Orval and Ard Nev in the foreground with the sharper peaks of the Rum Cuillin beyond

Most of the landscape of Rum was shaped by the formation of a volcano during the Palaeogene Period, some 60 million years ago. In the south of the island, the jagged peaks of the Rum Cuillin are obviously formed from rocks that are quite different from those that underlie the rounded hills to the west. However, all these different rocks represent the deeply eroded roots of the ancient volcano.

In the west, the more rounded hills such as Orval are composed of pale-coloured granite, which has been worn smooth by the action of wind, water and ice. The more jagged peaks of the Rum Cuillin are composed of darker, rougher rocks called gabbros. In the next section, we will look at how these different rocks formed deep in the Earth's crust beneath the Rum volcano.

Explosive Eruptions and Pyroclastic Flows

Outcrops of breccia in Coire Dubh

Volcanic activity on Rum began with molten rock, or magma, rising up through cracks in the Earth's crust. This molten rock collected in a magma chamber, a few kilometres below the surface of the Earth. As the amount of magma in the chamber increased, the rocks above were pushed upwards, forming a dome over a kilometre high and a few kilometres across. Evidence for the existence of this dome can still be seen on the slopes of the Rum Cuillin, where the layers in the Torridonian rocks are inclined steeply away from the adjacent igneous rocks.

Eventually, the pressure on the domed rocks became too great and they cracked, producing a series of fractures around the dome. The rocks of the dome collapsed downwards, forming a massive, roughly circular crater known as a caldera. The walls of this caldera were unstable, and so the floor of the caldera gradually became covered with the debris of rockfalls and landslides. This debris, which consisted largely of blocks and pebbles of Torridonian sandstone and Lewisian gneiss, was gradually compressed to form rocks known as breccias that can be seen in Coire Dubh.

Magma continued to rise up into the magma chamber beneath the caldera, and was eventually erupted onto the Earth's surface. The erupting magma was silica-rich, thick and sticky, and so it did not flow out easily from the volcano; instead it was ejected in explosive eruptions, throwing out hot ash and fragments of volcanic rock that spread out across the caldera floor in searing-hot gas clouds known as pyroclastic flows. Several episodes of explosive volcanic activity occurred, each separated by further collapse of the caldera. The rocks that formed from these pyroclastic flows are called rhyodacites. They can be seen in various places around the margins of the Rum Cuillin, and they are particularly well exposed on the ridge between the summits of Ainshval and Sgurr nan Gillean.

A modern explosive eruption, on the island of Montserrat

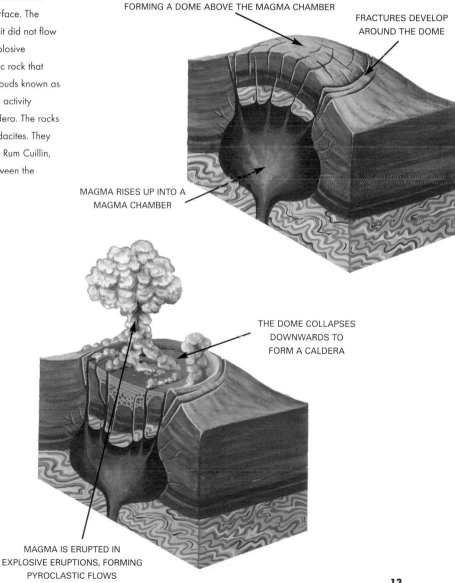

THE TORRIDONIAN SANDSTONES ARE PUSHED UPWARDS, FORMING A DOME ABOVE THE MAGMA CHAMBER

FRACTURES DEVELOP AROUND THE DOME

MAGMA RISES UP INTO A MAGMA CHAMBER

THE DOME COLLAPSES DOWNWARDS TO FORM A CALDERA

MAGMA IS ERUPTED IN EXPLOSIVE ERUPTIONS, FORMING PYROCLASTIC FLOWS

The Shaping of Western Rum

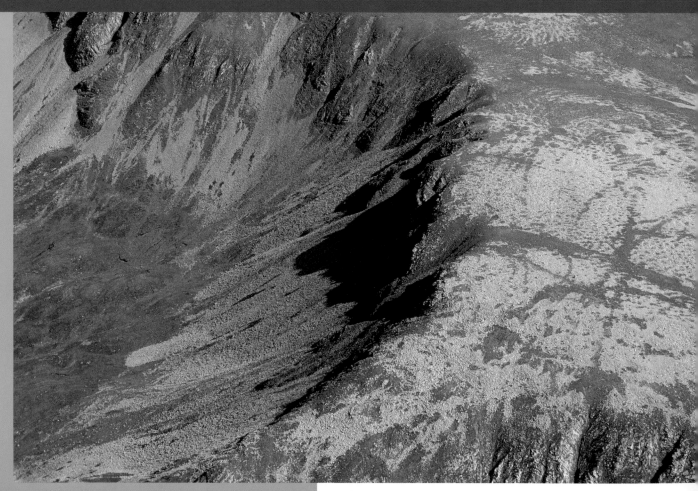

Aerial view of the western granite hills

Not all the silica-rich magma in the magma chamber was erupted, and some of it crystallised below the Earth's surface. The rate at which the magma cooled below the Earth's surface was slow, allowing large crystals to form, and this produced coarse-grained rocks called granites. The best examples of granites on Rum are in the western hills, particularly Orval and Ard Nev.

Mixed contact between pink granites and dark gabbros on the southeast side of Harris Bay

As the silica-rich magma was being erupted onto the surface, a slightly different type of magma was rising up into the magma chamber below. This magma was richer in iron and magnesium than the magma which formed the granites. It crystallised below the surface to form the gabbros and associated rocks that make up the more jagged peaks of the Rum Cuillin.

The contact between the granitic rocks of western Rum, and the gabbros of the Cuillin, can be seen on the southeast side of Harris Bay. Here, the darker gabbros and the pale pink granites became mixed up before they cooled and solidified, so that blocks of darker gabbro are surrounded by areas of pink granite.

From Molten Rock to Manx Shearwaters – The Rum Cuillin

Layered gabbros and peridotites on the western slopes of the Rum Cuillin

It is immediately apparent to anyone looking at the peaks of Askival and Hallival that these are formed of an unusual type of igneous rock, because the mountainsides are characterised by a distinct layering structure. Pale coloured layers of very hard rock, standing out as distinct cliffs a few metres high, are separated by layers of brown, much more crumbly rock on which grassy slopes have formed. This layering formed as the magmas cooled and crystallised in the magma chamber.

As magma cools, crystals gradually form within it – like ice crystals beginning to form in water as it freezes – until the magma has solidified into rock. In the Rum magma chamber, the first crystals that formed were composed of a type of magnesium and iron-rich mineral called olivine. These crystals were denser than the hot magma and so they sank towards the base of the magma chamber, accumulating as a distinct layer. These are the brown crumbly layers, which are made of a rock called peridotite.

On Askival and Hallival, the igneous layering is extremely regular, and has been studied by many geologists as a type example of this phenomenon. However, in some parts of Rum, particularly around Long Loch, the structures in the gabbros and peridotites are much more chaotic. In some places, randomly orientated blocks of layered gabbro are enclosed within structureless peridotite, whilst in other places the layering in the rocks is fantastically contorted. These structures formed in the magma chamber, when the piles of crystals built up until they became unstable. Blocks of solidified rock, together with loose crystals mixed with still-molten magma, avalanched down the sides of the magma chamber to create a chaotic mixture that eventually solidified to form the rocks we see today.

As the magma continued to cool, different minerals began to crystallise, and this led to the formation of the paler, harder layers. These layers are made of gabbro, a rock that here consists chiefly of olivine together with white crystals of feldspar. Then, a new batch of hot magma would be introduced into the magma chamber, and the next set of layers would begin to form.

The presence of this igneous layering has led to the presence of one of Rum's most well known features – the breeding colony of Manx shearwaters, one of the largest such colonies in the world. The shearwaters burrow into the soft, crumbly peridotite layers on the peaks of Askival, Hallival and Trollaval.

As well as the large-scale layers, small-scale layering can be seen in the rocks when they are examined closely. In places thin dark layers of a mineral called chromite can be found within the rocks, and some of these layers contain minerals rich in the platinum group of elements.

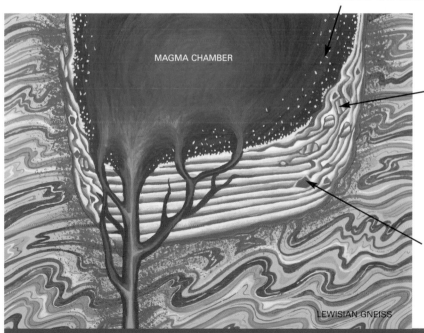

CRYSTALS FORM AND SINK TO THE BASE OF THE MAGMA CHAMBER

MAGMA CHAMBER

BLOCKS OF LAYERED ROCK AND CRYSTALS AVALANCHE DOWN THE SIDE OF THE MAGMA CHAMBER

CRYSTALS ACCUMULATE, FORMING LAYERS

LEWISIAN GNEISS

The development of layered gabbros in a magma chamber

Flowing Lavas

Aerial view showing the contrast between darker lavas on Fionchra, on the left of the picture, and the paler granite hills to the right

We do not know if any of the gabbro magma was erupted from the Rum volcano; if it was erupted, the resulting basalt lavas have long since been eroded away. However, lavas that were erupted from later volcanoes – possibly those on Skye and Mull – can be seen in the west of Rum, where they form the top parts of the hills of Fionchra, Orval and Bloodstone Hill. On the west side of Fionchra, the lavas have cooled into a columnar structure like that at the Giant's Causeway in Northern Ireland. These lavas lie on top of sedimentary rocks called conglomerates, which contain many rounded pebbles, laid down in rivers flowing across the land surface before the lavas were formed.

The pebbles in the conglomerates actually include pieces of Rum gabbro, and this tells us that the conglomerates, and thus the lavas on top of them, are younger than the igneous rocks of the Rum Cuillin. When the lavas were erupted, they flowed down the ancient river valleys, and the shapes of these valleys can still be seen today, particularly on the slopes of Bloodstone Hill.

At Bloodstone Hill, holes and cracks in the rock are filled with green agate which contains many tiny red flecks, and is thus known as bloodstone. This agate is composed mostly of silica, and was formed from heated water flowing through the rocks. This water dissolved minerals from the surrounding rocks, then precipitated them again into cracks when it cooled. The red flecks are tiny crystals of iron minerals, which have been oxidised on exposure to air, turning red.

Bloodstone Hill, with its distinctive summit cap of lavas

Eigg

The distinctive profile of the Sgùrr of Eigg

The islands of Eigg and Muck lie to the south east of Rum. Both islands are largely formed of lavas, which represent the remnants of what was once a much larger lava field, erupted from a slightly older volcano than Rum. The ridge of An Sgùrr dominates the skyline of Eigg. It provides an intriguing glimpse into the final phases of the volcanic activity in this part of Scotland. Great thicknesses of basalt lava had already been spewed out, creating a raw and inhospitable landscape. Thick layers of conglomerates containing water-rounded pebbles lie in a valley on top of these lavas, marking the location of an ancient water course. As volcanic activity in the area came to an end, a nearby volcano erupted sticky lava of unusual composition which flowed slowly along this ancient river bed. Over time this lava, which is known as pitchstone, cooled and developed impressive organ-pipe-like columns many tens of metres high.

Basalt columns on the east coast of Eigg, with the Sgùrr of Eigg beyond

The pioneering Victorian geologist Hugh Miller visited Eigg in 1844. He made some amazing discoveries during his short stay on the island. The rocks at sea level have yielded the fossilised remains of some long extinct animals such as marine turtles, crocodiles and most prized of all, plesiosaurs, more commonly known as the sea dragon. These layers of rock, which are of Jurassic age, accumulated on the floor of a sub-tropical lagoon that pre-dated the Rum volcano.

Canna and Sanday - Where Rivers and Volcanoes Meet

Right: layers of lava build Canna. A raised beach can be seen in the foreground

Left: sea stack made of lava and conglomerate Below: Dùn Mòr - a band of conglomerate towards the bottom of the stack is sandwiched between layers of lava

Canna and Sanday are composed largely of lavas, part of the major lava field that is exposed in northwestern Rum and extends to northern Skye. These basalt lavas were probably erupted from a major volcano on what is now the Isle of Skye. But what makes Canna of particular interest is that the area was traversed by fast-flowing rivers at the same time that the volcano was erupting. Great thicknesses of boulder conglomerate were deposited by this river. The boulders were rounded as they were carried along in the fast flowing river currents. Some are over a metre in diameter, indicating the strengths of the currents involved. Pebbles in these deposits have been matched with bedrock from Skye, suggesting that the river flowed from the north. These rocks were first studied by some of the early geological pioneers of Scottish geology, such as Archibald Geikie in 1897 and Alfred Harker ten years later.

22

The Ice Age

How Rum may have looked around 20,000 years ago: nunataks protruding through the present-day ice sheet in Greenland

Around 2.5 million years ago the Scottish climate descended into an Ice Age. The relatively stable subtropical climate of Neogene times was replaced by an unstable cold climate punctuated by short warmer episodes. About 750,000 years ago, the climate became even more severe. The extremely cold glacial periods lasted 100,000 years on average, whilst the warm interglacials were scarce and brief. Ice caps had plenty of time to accumulate and grow during these cold periods. During the most recent glacial period (the late Devensian), only 20,000 years ago, a great ice sheet covered almost the whole of northern Britain. The western Scottish Highlands were the major source of this ice.

At its maximum extent the last Scottish ice sheet overtopped all but the highest mountains in northwest Scotland. The highest summits on Rum would also have been ice-free, forming nunataks like those seen today in coastal parts of Greenland. At this time the Scottish ice sheet would have been up to 1000 metres thick on the mainland to the east of Rum.

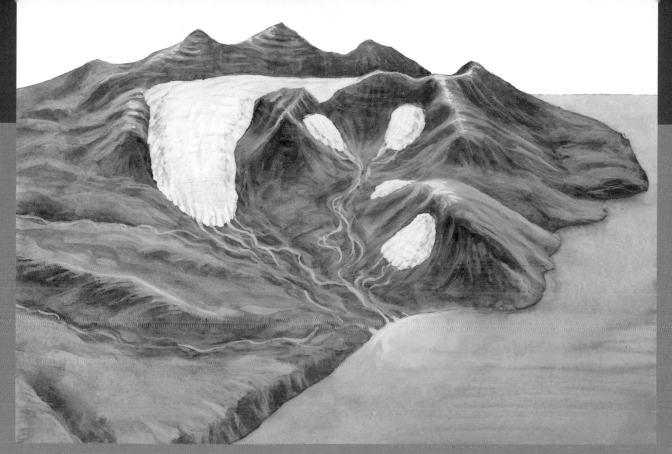

Artist's impression of the Rum Cuillin during the Loch Lomond Stadial, showing the corrie glaciers

The ice was channelled westwards through deep fjords such as Loch Broom, Loch Hourn and Loch Nevis, and streamed across the Small Isles, being deflected slightly around the mountains on Rum.

Following a sudden climatic warming around 14,700 years ago the ice sheet in northwest Scotland started to melt rapidly. The glaciers retreated back into the mountains and plants colonised the low ground. This brief warm spell lasted almost 1500 years and was comparable to the climate we know today. However, the respite was short lived. Around 13,000 years ago temperatures fell markedly and arctic conditions returned once more. This brief glacial spell (the Loch Lomond Stadial) brought small ice caps back to the high ground in northwest Scotland.

Rum nourished its own glaciers during this time, in the corries of the Cuillin and the western hills.

Only in the last 11,000 years has northwest Scotland been completely ice free. Following the last glaciation, the climate of Rum warmed extremely rapidly – summer temperatures possibly rising by 5 to 10°C in less than 100 years! Warm, moist, interglacial conditions have prevailed on the island ever since. After the retreat of the ice, Rum was rapidly colonised by vegetation, with the development of juniper scrub followed by birch and hazel woodland.

Glacial Clues and Patterns in the Stones

An ice-smoothed roche moutonnée in central Rum

Evidence of glaciation is immediately striking on the Isle of Rum. The landscape provides a superb record of the mighty glacial forces that have carved the rugged rocks into smooth U-shaped glens and deep corries. Rocks embedded in the base of the ice sheet scoured and abraded the valley sides, smoothing any sharp obstacles in their path.

Roche moutonnées – ice-smoothed bedrock hummocks – are found to the south of Kinloch Glen and indicate that ice once flowed from east to west. Upon closer examination, these streamlined rocks are covered in small scratches or striae – clues that the ice was once at work here.

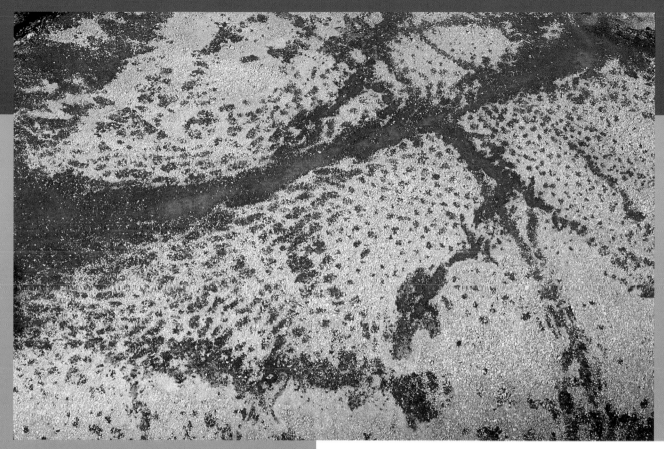

As the ice sheet melted it deposited huge boulders, some composed of rock types not found anywhere on Rum. These erratics can only have come from the Scottish mainland – yet more clues that a vast ice sheet once covered the island. Later, smaller glaciers deposited coarse gravelly debris mixed with silt and sand. This material forms moraines where the ice margin readvanced over the debris, bulldozing it up to form a ridge in front of the glacier. Good examples are found in Glen Dibidil in the southwest of the island.

Although glaciers once covered almost the entire island, the tops of the highest mountains probably remained ice-free throughout the last glacial period. On these peaks, intense frost shattering in the extreme cold created blockfields of loose, sharp, broken rock. Some of these blockfields tumbled downslope to form screes. Over time the rock fragments have been broken down further into finer, soil-like, material. Freeze-thaw processes churn the soil and sort particles into curious regular patterns. Fine examples of these stone stripes and polygons occur near the summit of Orval. These features are still actively forming – proof that the conditions on Rum are still cold enough for ice to grow in the ground even today!

High and Dry

The raised beach at Harris Bay, Rum

The beach at Kilmory Bay,
with the Isle of Skye beyond

The Isle of Rum has witnessed a complicated history of sea-level rise and fall over the last million years or so. This is reflected in the geomorphology of the island's rugged, spectacular coastline.

Where the land presently meets the sea has been the coastline on Rum for only a few thousand years. High above the waves, 30 to 40 m in fact, is a rock platform that encircles almost the entire island. This represents Rum's oldest coastline and was cut by waves around 100,000 years ago (before the last glacial period), when the sea level was much higher than it is now.

At the time of the last major glacial period, sea level across the Inner Hebrides was still higher than today. As the Scottish ice sheet thinned and the glaciers rapidly retreated, a great weight of ice was removed from the land and so the Earth's crust locally began to rise.

Rebounding of the land caused the relative sea level on Rum to fall, even though the actual volume of water in the ocean had increased due to the melting ice. The raised beaches and abandoned shorelines left high and dry are the legacy of these once higher sea levels. The raised beach at Harris on the west coast of Rum is 30 m above the present-day tidemark. Similar but smaller abandoned beach fragments are found at Kilmory Bay in the north and at Loch Scresort in the east of the island.

Once the rate of crustal uplift had slowed almost to a halt, sea level around Rum began to rise. Evidence of this is seen at Harris, Kilmory and Guirdil bays where a second set of raised beaches are set back from the present-day storm beach. These post-glacial beaches, at 5 to 6 m above the high-tide mark, formed around 6000 years ago. Although not noticeable, the sea level on Rum is still falling slowly as the island gradually rises!

Early People on Rum –
Exploiting the Island's Natural Resources

The earliest people on Rum arrived in the Stone Age, and one of their main settlements was on the shores of Loch Scresort, close to the present village of Kinloch. Dating from almost 9000 years ago, this is among the earliest known settlements anywhere in Scotland. These people would have been nomadic hunter-gatherers, and one of the reasons for their settling on Rum may have been the availability of useful natural resources. Agates from Bloodstone Hill played an important part in the early history of Rum. The agate, or bloodstone, is hard but fractures easily and smoothly. It is similar to flint, which is rare in northwest Scotland, and so it was used to make tools of many kinds, including arrowheads, scrapers and blades. Rum bloodstone was an important resource at this time and it is found on a variety of sites from Ardnamurchan to the Inner Sound, which indicates that the Stone Age inhabitants obviously had wider connections.

By 4000 years ago, people on Rum were farming some of the sheltered glens, and still making use of bloodstone for tools. Bronze Age cairns have been recognised at places such as Guirdil and Harris, and Iron Age forts at Kilmory and Shellesder.

Christianity arrived on Rum in the 7th century AD, following the founding of St Columba's monastery on Iona in the 6th century. Sandstone pillars incised with crosses have been found at Bagh na h-Uamha and Kilmory, and there may have been a chapel at Kilmory. However, many of the place names on the island date back to the Vikings – names such as Askival, Dibidil, Hallival, and Trollaval all betray their Norse origins. Some of these names have subsequently passed into the geological literature, with terms such as 'allivalite' used for the type of gabbro that appears on Hallival. Rum was under the rule of the Vikings from the 9th to the 12th centuries, and then became part of the kingdom of the Lords of the Isles.

9,000 year old stone blades found on the Isle of Rum

Eighth century
Christian cross made
of sandstone, at
Bagh na h-Uamha, Rum

The Bulloughs and SNH

The first geologists visited the Isle of Rum in the early 19th century, and were fascinated by what they found. John MacCulloch went to Rum during research for his account of the geological structure of the Western Isles of Scotland, published in 1819. His description of Rum in this book begins thus: "Although the rough and dangerous shores, the trackless surface, and the perennial rain of this island, are repulsive to the general traveller, the geologist will here meet with appearances of such interest, as to induce him to brave its tempests and to defy the toil which he must encounter in its investigation".

Only a few years after MacCulloch's visit, people were largely cleared off Rum to make way for sheep, but this venture was unprofitable. The island then passed through the hands of a series of wealthy landowners, who used it as a sporting estate. In 1888 the island was bought by a wealthy industrialist, John Bullough. It was his son George Bullough who built the stately pile of Kinloch Castle in 1900, shipping red sandstone all the way from Arran rather than using local building materials from Rum. The story goes that the workmen building the castle were paid extra to wear kilts! The Bullough family made use of the island as a private retreat until 1957, when it was sold to the forerunner of SNH, the Nature Conservancy Council, and became a National Nature Reserve. Since then it has been managed for nature conservation purposes including red deer research, sea eagle reintroduction, and woodland restoration.

Kinloch Castle

The Landscape Today

An aerial view south-eastwards over
Canna with Rum in the background

From the tops of its pyramidal peaks, Rum offers a spectacular panorama encompassing the sloping backbone of Eigg, the rich green pasture of diminutive Muck and the carved basalt coastline embracing Canna and the low lying Sanday.

Held together by the sea, these islands combine a richness of landform, colour and texture with ever-changing light and dramatic weather. The landscape can feel dark and oppressive in the fading greyness of winter, or spangled with intense light and distant clarity on a brilliant summer day.

The Rum Cuillin with the Isle of Canna beyond

From sandy beaches to coastal stacks, from remote ridges to clustered houses and from windswept woodland to flowering machair, these islands are a microcosm of the Scottish landscape. Their outstanding natural beauty has led them to be designated as one of our National Scenic Areas.

Each island has its distinctive pattern of habitation and cultivation. Fertile grassy slopes support crofts on Canna and a farm on Muck. The largest of the islands, Rum, is dominated by its rugged mountains, rough terrain and uninhabited glens. Eigg combines managed land with woodland and scattered houses. All of the islands focus much of their settlement on the sheltered east facing harbours.

The islands are perhaps best known as the familiar silhouettes seen from the mainland or neighbouring Skye – the low wedge of Muck, the flat topped tower of the Sgùrr of Eigg, the massed peaks and ridges of Rum and the whale-like profile of Canna.

Scottish Natural Heritage
and the British Geological Survey

Scottish Natural Heritage is a government body. Its aim is to help people enjoy Scotland's natural heritage responsibly, understand it more fully and use it wisely so that it can be sustained for future generations.

Scottish Natural Heritage
12 Hope Terrace
Edinburgh EH9 2AS

SCOTTISH
NATURAL
HERITAGE

The British Geological Survey maintains up-to-date knowledge of the geology of the UK and its continental shelf. It carries out surveys and geological research.
The Scottish Office of BGS is sited in Edinburgh. The office runs an advisory and information service, a geological library and a well-stocked geological bookshop.

British Geological Survey
Murchison House
West Mains Road
Edinburgh EH9 3LA

British
Geological Survey
NATURAL ENVIRONMENT RESEARCH COUNCIL

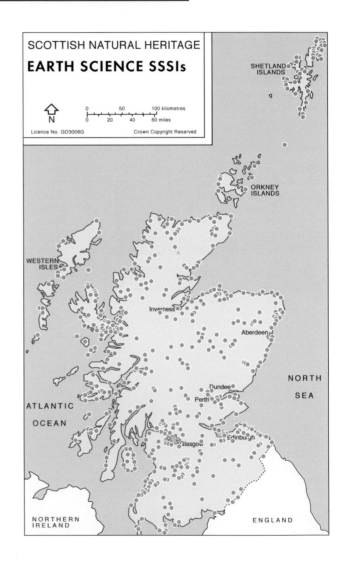

SCOTTISH NATURAL HERITAGE
EARTH SCIENCE SSSIs

N

0   50   100 kilometres
0 20   40   60 miles

Licence No. GD3006G   Crown Copyright Reserved

SHETLAND ISLANDS

ORKNEY ISLANDS

WESTERN ISLES

Inverness

Aberdeen

ATLANTIC OCEAN

Dundee

Perth

NORTH SEA

Glasgow   Edinburgh

NORTHERN IRELAND

ENGLAND

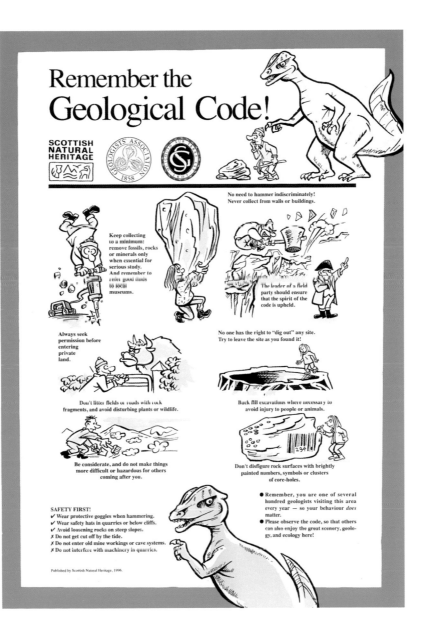

Remember the Geological Code!

SCOTTISH NATURAL HERITAGE

Keep collecting to a minimum: remove fossils, rocks or minerals only when essential for serious study. And remember to refer good finds to local museums.

No need to hammer indiscriminately! Never collect from walls or buildings.

The leader of a field party should ensure that the spirit of the code is upheld.

Always seek permission before entering private land.

No one has the right to "dig out" any site. Try to leave the site as you found it!

Don't litter fields or roads with rock fragments, and avoid disturbing plants or wildlife.

Back fill excavations where necessary to avoid injury to people or animals.

Be considerate, and do not make things more difficult or hazardous for others coming after you.

Don't disfigure rock surfaces with brightly painted numbers, symbols or clusters of core-holes.

SAFETY FIRST!
✔ Wear protective goggles when hammering.
✔ Wear safety hats in quarries or below cliffs.
✔ Avoid loosening rocks on steep slopes.
✗ Do not get cut off by the tide.
✗ Do not enter old mine workings or cave systems.
✗ Do not interfere with machinery in quarries.

● Remember, you are one of several hundred geologists visiting this area every year — so your behaviour *does* matter.
● Please observe the code, so that others can also enjoy the great scenery, geology, and ecology here!

Published by Scottish Natural Heritage, 1996.

Arran and the Clyde Islands

The diverse landscapes of Arran and the Clyde Islands mark the boundary between Highland and Lowland. Discover the ancient secrets and the appeal of these well-loved islands.
David McAdam & Steve Robertson
ISBN 1 85397 287 8 pbk 24pp £3.00

Cairngorms

Their broad plateaux, steep sided glens and deep corries make the Cairngorms one of the foremost mountain landscapes in Britain. Discover how they were fashioned by weathering, glaciers and rivers.
John Gordon, Vanessa Brazier,
Rob Threadgold & Sarah Keast
ISBN 1 85397 086 7 pbk 28pp £2.00

East Lothian and the Borders

Underneath the calm facade of south east Scotland's fertile plains and rolling hills lies a complex structure, which reflects an eventful geological history.
David McAdam & Phil Stone
ISBN 1 85397 242 8 pbk 26pp £3.00

Edinburgh and West Lothian

The tranquil appearance of the city of Edinburgh nestling between the surrounding hills and the undulating countryside of West Lothian belies their dramatic volcanic past.
David McAdam
ISBN 1 85397 327 0 pbk 44pp £4.95

Fife and Tayside

The dramatic coastline and volcanic hills of Fife and Tayside are testiment to the dramatic geological past. The story is set at a time when Scotland sat astride the equator.
Mike Browne, Alan McKirdy & David McAdam
ISBN 1 85397 110 3 pbk 36pp £3.95

Glen Roy

This book tells the story of how the Parallel Roads formed and reveals a fascinating picture of how ice age glaciers and ice dammed lakes shaped the landscape of the West Highlands. Douglas Peacock, Frank May & John Gordon
ISBN 1 85397 360 2 pbk 48pp £4.95

Loch Lomond to Stirling

The heart of Scotland encompasses some of the most diverse landscapes in Scotland. From the low Carse to the mountain tops - find out how these modern landscapes reflect the geological changes of the past.
Mike Browne & John Mendum
ISBN 1 85397 119 7 pbk 26pp £2.00

Northwest Highlands

Providing an ancient bulwark to Atlantic storms, the stunning scenery we see today in Northwest Highlands was created by the dramatic collision of continents. This book tells a dramatic tale of Scotland's journey through time - our links to Canada, Greenland and Scandinavia and the exploits of the early geological explorers. In explaining our rocky past, it also shows why this region is so important to geologists today.
John Mendum, Jon Merritt & Alan McKirdy
ISBN 1 85397 139 1 pbk 52pp £6.95

Orkney and Shetland

These northern outposts of Scotland hold a great fascination for the geologist. Starting 3 billion years ago, their story tells of colliding continents, bizarre lifeforms and a landscape which continues to be eroded by the pounding force of the Atlantic.
Clive Auton, Terry Fletcher & David Gould ISBN 1 85397 220 7 pbk 24pp £2.50

Skye

Skye is one of Scotland's most popular tourist destinations, and deservedly so. But what would Skye be without the jagged peaks of the Cuillins or the intriguing rock formations of the Quiraing? In many ways it is the geology of Skye that attracts its visitors and this booklet helps you to understand how the mountains, rocks and lochs were formed.
David Stephenson & Jon Merritt ISBN 1 85397 026 3 pbk 24pp £2.50

Scotland: the creation of its natural landscape

Scotland: the Creation of its Natural Landscape provides a wealth of information on how Scotland was created and the events that took place there through the aeons. But the story doesn't stop back in the mists of time, it continually unfolds and this book provides up to the minute information on geological events taking place beneath our feet. It also provides a history of geological science and highlights the enormous contribution Scots geologists have made to the world.
Alan McKirdy & Roger Crofts ISBN 1 85397 004 2 pbk 64pp £7.50

Series Editor: Alan McKirdy (SNH)

Other books soon to be produced in the series include:
• Mull and Iona • Glasgow

SNH Publication Order Form

Title	Price	Quantity
Arran & the Clyde Islands	£3.00	
Cairngorms	£2.00	
East Lothian & the Borders	£3.00	
Edinburgh & West Lothian	£4.95	
Fife & Tayside	£4.95	
Glen Roy	£x.xx	
Loch Lomond to Stirling	£2.00	
Northwest Highlands	£6.95	
Orkney & Shetland	£2.50	
Skye	£3.95	
Scotland. the Creation of its natural landscape	£7.50	

Postage and packaging: free of charge within the UK.

A standard charge of £2.95 will be applied to all orders from the EU.

Elsewhere a standard charge of £5.50 will apply.

Please complete in **BLOCK CAPITALS**

Name _____

Address _____

_____

_____

Post Code

Type of Credit Card   VISA ☐   EUROCARD MasterCard ☐

Name of card holder _____

Card Number ☐☐☐☐ ☐☐☐☐ ☐☐☐☐ ☐☐☐☐

Expiry Date ☐☐ ☐☐

Send order and cheque made payable to Scottish Natural Heritage to:
Scottish Natural Heritage, Design and Publications, Battleby, Redgorton,
Perth PH1 3EW
E-mail: pubs@redgore.demon.co.uk   www.snh.org.uk

We may want to send you details of other SNH publications, please tick the
box below if you do not want this. We will not pass your details to anyone else.

I do not wish to receive information on SNH publications ☐

Please add my name to the mailing list for the   SNH Magazine ☐

Publications Catalogue ☐